Kids'
Passport®
To Your National Parks
Companion

TABLE OF CONTENTS

Grant-Kohrs Ranch NHS

HOW TO USE THIS BOOK

Welcome to the amazing world of your national parks. This book was developed just for you, to use with the *Passport To Your National Parks* book. Use it to explore the most interesting and important sites in the United States of America.

The *Passport To Your National Parks* booklet has information about the parks and gives you a place to keep your passport stamps. This booklet is a place for you to keep whatever **you** think is important from your park visit. Gather **ranger autographs**, keep track of your **Junior Ranger** programs, or write about your discoveries in your **field journal**.

This book is packed with ideas and cool facts to make your park visits even more special. **Grab your Passport and get out there!**

This booklet is a companion to the *Passport To Your National Parks* booklet. The *Passport* booklet has information, photos, and maps of our national parks. It also has places to collect the series of *Passport* stamps issued each year. When you visit a national park you can get your book canceled. The ink cancellation mark records the date you visited a particular park. For more information about the *Passport* program visit **www.eParks.com**.

THE MISSION

The National Park Service has a mission — that means a job we are all working to complete every day, through everything we do. When you visit the parks, and treat them well, you help us accomplish that mission.

So what is the mission?
The National Park Service preserves unimpaired the natural and cultural resources and values of the National Park System for the enjoyment of this and future generations. The National Park Service cooperates with partners to extend the benefits of cultural and natural resource conservation and outdoor recreation throughout the country and the world.

In this way, the parks are like library books. They are yours to visit and enjoy, but please leave them beautiful and complete for the next visitor to enjoy.

THE ARROWHEAD

What does it mean?

The National Park Service Arrowhead can be found throughout the United States and the territories of American Samoa, Guam, Puerto Rico, and the U.S. Virgin Islands. It is recognized around the world as a symbol of conservation of nature's wonders and America's cultural heritage.

The arrowhead shape stands for all of the **cultural and historic sites** in the National Park System.

The trees stand for all the **plants** in the parks, while the buffalo represents the **animals**. The mountains and the lake are here to remind us of the **scenic beauty** of the parks, and the **land and water** that sustains all those plants and animals.

WHAT KIND OF PARK?

The different types of "units" within the National Park System sometimes confuse visitors. Congress picks the names when they create the sites. The president, who can create national monuments, can also name them. Many names tell what the parks are — lakeshores, seashores, battlefields — but others cannot be so easily explained because so many different types of parks are included in each category. The most important thing to remember is that in 1970, Congress said that the 1916 National Park Service Organic Act meant that all units of the National Park System are equally important under the law.

Why is that important? It means that the historic site near your town is just as important as the big parks like Yellowstone or the Grand Canyon. All are part of telling the story of this nation.

Types of Parks:

National Park:
These are large, natural places which usually include significant parts of the story of America. National parks are established by Congress.

Yosemite NP

Devils Tower NM

National Monument:
The Antiquities Act of 1906 authorized the president to declare that landmarks, structures, and other objects of historic or scientific importance should be national monuments.

National Preserve:
National preserves are like national parks, but in these areas, Congress has permitted hunting, trapping, oil/gas exploration, and other activities.

Big Thicket N PRES

National Historic Site:
Usually, a national historic site is the location of a single home or small area from an important time in history. The name usually tells what makes the place important.

Little Rock Central High School NHS

Jean Lafitte NHP

National Historical Park:
This designation generally applies to historic parks that are more than single places or buildings. They are usually bigger than national historic sites and have a variety of stories to tell.

National Memorial:
A national memorial is in remembrance of a historic person or event. Memorials are public places where all people can visit and remember important events and people in America's past.

Mount Rushmore N MEM

National Battlefield:
This includes national battlefield, national battlefield park, national battlefield site, and national military park. These

Fort Donelson NB

are places where important battles were fought.

Antietam NB

National Cemetery:
There are presently 14 national cemeteries in the National Park System. All of them are linked to battlefields or historic sites. Soldiers and other important Americans are buried here.

National Recreation Area:
Most of these areas are located on large lakes or reservoirs where there is a lot of water-based recreation. The others are located near major population centers, and

Big South Fork NRRA

are great places for people who live in cities to visit, hike, and play.

National Seashore:
There are ten national seashores on the Atlantic, Gulf, and Pacific coasts. They protect ocean and shore environments and provide a place to come and enjoy the outdoors.

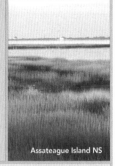
Assateague Island NS

National Lakeshore:
National lakeshores are all on the Great Lakes. They are very much like the seashores.

Sleeping Bear Dunes NL

National River:
These rivers are set aside for their recreation, natural scenic beauty, and the wildlife that depends on the river for life.

Mississippi NRRA

George Washington MEM PKWY

National Parkway:
The word "parkway" refers to a road and the parkland along each side of the road. All parkways were intended for scenic driving, and often connect to other park sites.

National Trail:
Historic trails follow the footsteps of explorers and settlers. Scenic trails lead visitors through America's most beautiful landscapes.

Lewis and Clark NHT

Other Designations:
Some units of the National Park System have unique titles or combinations of titles, like Rock Creek Park and Prince William Forest Park.

FUN FACT: *Did you know that your National Park System includes volcanoes, glaciers, coral reefs, and dinosaur fossils?*

What Kind of Park?

What kind of park would you create?
Use this space to describe or draw your
national park.

Badlands NP

WHERE CAN I GO?

Your national parks are home to America's amazing sights, sounds, and stories. There is something for everyone to share and enjoy. If you are interested in natural beauty, the parks have the best our nation has to offer. If history is more your style, many parks are home to the stories of people and places that made this country what it is today. Whatever your interest, check the following pages for parks you might like to visit.

Park Abbreviations

IHS	International Historic Site
NB	National Battlefield
NBP	National Battlefield Park
NBS	National Battlefield Site
NHP	National Historical Park
NHP & E PRES	Nat'l Historical Park & Ecological Preserve
NHP & PRES	Nat'l Historical Park & Preserve
NH RES	National Historical Reserve
NHS	National Historic Site
NHT	National Historic Trail
NL	National Lakeshore
NM	National Monument
NM & PRES	National Monument & Preserve
NMP	National Military Park
N MEM	National Memorial
NP	National Park
N & SP	National & State Parks
NP & PRES	National Park & Preserve
N PRES	National Preserve
NR	National River
NRA	National Recreation Area
NRR	National Recreation River
NRRA	Nat'l River & Recreation Area
N RES	National Reserve
NS	National Seashore
NSR	Nat'l Scenic River or Riverway
NST	National Scenic Trail
PKWY	Parkway
SRR	Scenic & Recreational River
WR	Wild River
WSR	Wild & Scenic River

Stories of Native Peoples, Yesterday and Today

Through the stories of the national parks are woven the heritage of Native Americans, Alaska Natives, and Pacific Islanders. By visiting these parks, you will learn stories from the past, and also experience these vibrant living cultures.

Washita Battlefield NHS

PARKS VISITED (Check box if you have been to the park)

PARK NAME	STATE
☐ Cape Krusenstern NM	Alaska
☐ Canyon de Chelly NM	Arizona
☐ Casa Grande Ruins NM	Arizona
☐ Hohokam Pima NM	Arizona

PARK NAME	STATE
Hubbell Trading Post NHS	Arizona
Montezuma Castle NM	Arizona
Navajo NM	Arizona
Pipe Spring NM	Arizona
Tonto NM	Arizona
Tuzigoot NM	Arizona
Walnut Canyon NM	Arizona
Wupatki NM	Arizona
Mesa Verde NP	Colorado
Yucca House NM	Colorado
Timucuan Ecol. & Hist. Pres.	Florida
Kaloko-Honokohau NHP	Hawaii
Pu'uhonua o Honaunau NHP	Hawaii
Pu'ukohola Heiau NHS	Hawaii
Nez Perce NHP	Idaho
Effigy Mounds NM	Iowa
Poverty Point NM	Louisiana
Pipestone NM	Minnesota
Little Bighorn Battlefield NM	Montana
Aztec Ruins NM	New Mexico
Bandelier NM	New Mexico
Chaco Culture NHP	New Mexico
Gila Cliff Dwellings NM	New Mexico
Petroglyph NM	New Mexico
Knife River Indian Villages NHS	North Dakota
Hopewell Culture NHP	Ohio
Washita Battlefield NHS	Oklahoma
Hovenweep NM	Utah

Stories about African Americans

You can learn more about our African American heritage by visiting the places where it happened. The park stories are more than just history — parks tell the stories of musicians and scientists and great writers and speakers. African American heritage is part of the stories told in many of your national parks. Here are a few places with particularly strong links to that heritage.

Frederick Douglass

	PARK NAME	STATE
☐	Selma to Montgomery NHT	Alabama
☐	Tuskegee Airmen NHS	Alabama
☐	Tuskegee Institute NHS	Alabama
☐	Martin Luther King, Jr. NHS	Georgia
☐	Nicodemus NHS	Kansas
☐	Boston African American NHS	Massachusetts
☐	African Burial Ground NM	New York
☐	Booker T. Washington NM	Virginia
☐	Maggie L. Walker NHS	Virginia
☐	Frederick Douglass NHS	Wash., D.C.
☐	Mary McLeod Bethune Council House NHS	Wash., D.C.

PARKS VISITED

Agate Fossil Beds NM

Really Old Stories

Did you know that dinosaurs once lived in this country? You can see the fossils of these huge creatures, as well as the fossils of tiny insects in these national parks. While you're looking, check out the petrified forests and delicate plants preserved for all time in layers of stone.

PARKS VISITED

PARK NAME	STATE
☐ Petrified Forest NP	Arizona
☐ Dinosaur NM	Colorado
☐ Hagerman Fossil Beds NM	Idaho
☐ Agate Fossil Beds NM	Nebraska
☐ John Day Fossil Beds NM	Oregon
☐ Guadalupe Mountains NP	Texas
☐ Capitol Reef NP	Utah
☐ Fossil Butte NM	Wyoming

Stories about Our War for Independence

Our War for Independence, the American Revolution, left its mark on the land in some surprising places. Here are some of the best places to learn about our fight for independence from the British.

Park rangers often dress in historical costumes to help tell the stories of America's past.

Morristown NHP

PARKS VISITED

	PARK NAME	STATE
☐	George Rogers Clark NHP	Indiana
☐	Thomas Stone NHS	Maryland
☐	Boston NHP	Massachusetts
☐	Minute Man NHP	Massachusetts
☐	Morristown NHP	New Jersey

	PARK NAME	STATE
☐	Fort Stanwix NM	New York
☐	Saint Paul's Church NHS	New York
☐	Saratoga NHP	New York
☐	Guilford Courthouse NMP	North Carolina
☐	Moores Creek NB	North Carolina
☐	Independence NHP	Pennsylvania
☐	Thaddeus Kosciuszko N MEM	Pennsylvania
☐	Valley Forge NHP	Pennsylvania
☐	Charles Pinckney NHS	South Carolina
☐	Cowpens NB	South Carolina
☐	Historic Camden Revolutionary War Site	South Carolina
☐	Kings Mountain NMP	South Carolina
☐	Ninety Six NHS	South Carolina
☐	Colonial NHP	Virginia
☐	Jamestown NHS	Virginia
☐	Yorktown Battlefield	Virginia

Thaddeus Kosciuszko N MEM

FUN FACT: *The smallest national park, Thaddeus Kosciuszko National Memorial in Philadelphia, is a single building.*

Civil War Stories

Brother fought brother in a war that ended slavery in America. The southern states broke away from the northern states, and the Civil War began. As bloody battles raged across the country, the stories were captured in the mountains, fields, and towns. Here are the places to go to learn about the time, the people, the war, and the peace.

PARKS VISITED

	PARK NAME	STATE
☐	Pea Ridge NMP	Arkansas
☐	Fort Point NHS	California
☐	Andersonville NHS	Georgia
☐	Chickamauga & Chattanooga NMP	Georgia
☐	Fort Pulaski NM	Georgia

	PARK NAME	STATE
☐	Kennesaw Mountain NBP	Georgia
☐	Antietam NB	Maryland
☐	Monocacy NB	Maryland
☐	Brices Cross Roads NBS	Mississippi
☐	Tupelo NB	Mississippi
☐	Vicksburg NMP	Mississippi
☐	Wilson's Creek NB	Missouri
☐	Gettysburg NMP	Pennsylvania
☐	Fort Sumter NM	South Carolina
☐	Fort Donelson NB	Tennessee
☐	Shiloh NMP	Tennessee
☐	Stones River NB	Tennessee
☐	Appomattox Court House NHP	Virginia
☐	Fredericksburg & Spotsylvania County Battlefields Memorial NMP	Virginia
☐	Manassas NBP	Virginia
☐	Petersburg NB	Virginia
☐	Richmond NBP	Virginia

FUN FACT: *Since 1910, filmmakers have been coming to national parks to capture history and majestic scenery for their movies.*

23

Stories that Built America

American history has something for everyone, because everyone played a part. Check this list of parks with stories of Americans of all ages, colors, and backgrounds. There are stories of children and elders, natives and immigrants. It's all waiting for you!

Hampton NHS

	PARK NAME	STATE
☐	Klondike Gold Rush NHP	Alaska
☐	Sitka NHP	Alaska
☐	Yukon-Charley Rivers N PRES	Alaska
☐	Tumacacori NHP	Arizona
☐	Hot Springs NP	Arkansas
☐	Little Rock Central High School NHS	Arkansas
☐	Alcatraz Island	California
☐	Cabrillo NM	California
☐	Ocmulgee NM	Georgia
☐	Kalaupapa NHP	Hawaii
☐	Brown v. Board of Education NHS	Kansas
☐	Cane River Creole NHP	Louisiana

PARKS VISITED

	PARK NAME	STATE
☐	Jean Lafitte NHP & PRES	Louisiana
☐	New Orleans Jazz NHP	Louisiana
☐	Saint Croix Island IHS	Maine
☐	Clara Barton NHS	Maryland
☐	Fort McHenry NM	Maryland
☐	Hampton NHS	Maryland
☐	Voyageurs NP	Minnesota
☐	Natchez NHP	Mississippi
☐	Pecos NHP	New Mexico
☐	Salinas Pueblo Missions NM	New Mexico
☐	Federal Hall N MEM	New York
☐	Lower East Side Tenement NHS	New York
☐	Statue of Liberty NM	New York
☐	Gloria Dei Church NHS	Pennsylvania
☐	Touro Synagogue NHS	Rhode Island
☐	Great Smoky Mountains NP	Tennessee
☐	Chamizal N MEM	Texas
☐	San Antonio Missions NHP	Texas
☐	Arlington House	Virginia
☐	Cedar Creek & Belle Grove NHP	Virginia
☐	Green Springs National Historic Landmark District	Virginia
☐	Salt River Bay NHP & E PRES	Virgin Islands
☐	Ebey's Landing NH RES	Washington
☐	Constitution Gardens	Wash., D.C.
☐	National Capital Parks	Wash., D.C.
☐	Pennsylvania Avenue NHS	Wash., D.C.
☐	Harpers Ferry NHP	West Virginia

The White House

Stories of American Presidents

Do you know what it takes to be President of the United States? Visit and learn! These sites are all about our presidents from childhood to the White House. Learn how they helped shape the nation. Will you be president someday?

PARKS VISITED

PARK NAME	STATE
☐ Jimmy Carter NHS	Georgia
☐ Lincoln Home NHS	Illinois
☐ Lincoln Boyhood N MEM	Indiana
☐ Herbert Hoover NHS	Iowa
☐ Abraham Lincoln Birthplace NHP	Kentucky

	PARK NAME	STATE
☐	Adams NHP	Massachusetts
☐	John F. Kennedy NHS	Massachusetts
☐	Harry S Truman NHS	Missouri
☐	Ulysses S. Grant NHS	Missouri
☐	Eleanor Roosevelt NHS	New York
☐	Hamilton Grange N MEM	New York
☐	Home of Franklin D. Roosevelt NHS	New York
☐	Martin Van Buren NHS	New York
☐	Sagamore Hill NHS	New York
☐	Theodore Roosevelt Birthplace NHS	New York
☐	Theodore Roosevelt Inaugural NHS	New York
☐	Theodore Roosevelt NP	North Dakota
☐	First Ladies NHS	Ohio
☐	James A. Garfield NHS	Ohio
☐	William Howard Taft NHS	Ohio
☐	Eisenhower NHS	Pennsylvania
☐	Mount Rushmore N MEM	South Dakota
☐	Andrew Johnson NHS	Tennessee
☐	Lyndon B. Johnson NHP	Texas
☐	George Washington Birthplace NM	Virginia
☐	Ford's Theatre NHS	Wash., D.C.
☐	Franklin D. Roosevelt MEM	Wash., D.C.
☐	Lincoln Memorial	Wash., D.C.
☐	Lyndon B. Johnson Memorial Grove	Wash., D.C.
☐	Theodore Roosevelt Island	Wash., D.C.
☐	Thomas Jefferson Memorial	Wash., D.C.
☐	Washington Monument	Wash., D.C.
☐	White House	Wash., D.C.

Stories from the Trail

Trails crossed this country long before roads, railroads, and planes. Take a hike on some of America's most amazing trails. Some of them challenge you to walk in the footsteps of settlers or explorers, while others guide you through the most beautiful countryside you will ever see. Come take a hike!

FUN FACT: The Appalachian and Pacific Crest trails were the first two trails established under the National Trails System Act of 1968.

PARK NAME	STATE
☐ Iditarod NHT	Alaska
☐ California NHT	California
☐ Juan Bautista de Anza NHT	California
☐ Pacific Crest NST	California
☐ Continental Divide NST	Colorado
☐ Florida NST	Florida
☐ Appalachian NST	Maine
☐ Natchez Trace NST	Mississippi
☐ Nez Perce NHT	Montana
☐ New Jersey Coastal Heritage Trail	New Jersey
☐ El Camino Real NHT	New Mexico
☐ Old Spanish NHT	New Mexico
☐ Santa Fe NHT	New Mexico
☐ Trail of Tears NHT	New Mexico
☐ Overmountain Victory NHT	South Carolina
☐ Mormon Pioneer NHT	Utah
☐ Oregon NHT	Utah
☐ Pony Express NHT	Utah
☐ Potomac Heritage NST	Wash., D.C.
☐ Ice Age NST	Wisconsin
☐ North Country NST	Wisconsin

River Stories

Rivers rush from the mountains to the sea, or wind slowly through wide valleys. Some tell the story of thousands of years of cutting, cutting...until a canyon appears. Each of these rivers has its own story and its own personality. Wouldn't you like to see them all?

PARKS VISITED

	PARK NAME	STATE
☐	Little River Canyon N PRES	Alabama
☐	Kobuk Wild River	Alaska
☐	Mulchatna Wild River	Alaska
☐	Noatak Wild River	Alaska
☐	Salmon Wild River	Alaska
☐	Tinayguk Wild River	Alaska
☐	Tlikakila Wild River	Alaska

	PARK NAME	STATE
☐	Buffalo NR	Arkansas
☐	Kern River	California
☐	Merced River	California
☐	Tuolumne River	California
☐	Farmington Nat'l WSR	Connecticut
☐	Sudbury, Assabet & Concord Nat'l WSR	Massachusetts
☐	Mississippi NRRA	Minnesota
☐	Ozark NSR	Missouri
☐	Flathead River	Montana
☐	Missouri NRR	Nebraska
☐	Niobrara NSR	Nebraska
☐	Lamprey WSR	New Hamp.
☐	Great Egg Harbor SRR	New Jersey
☐	Maurice SRR	New Jersey
☐	Lower Delaware WSR	Pennsylvania
☐	Middle Delaware NSR	Pennsylvania
☐	White Clay Creek WSR	Pennsylvania
☐	Rio Grande WSR	Texas
☐	Bluestone NSR	West Virginia
☐	New River Gorge NR	West Virginia
☐	Saint Croix NSR	Wisconsin

Stories of Famous Americans

America is home to inventors, artists, writers, and other talented people. These national parks tell the stories of their struggles to achieve their goals, and the stories of their successes. Will there be a park named after you someday?

FUN FACT:

You can visit Thomas Edison's laboratory and "Invention Factory" at Thomas Edison NHP in New Jersey.

Thomas Edison

Weir Farm NHS

PARK NAME	STATE
Eugene O'Neill NHS	California
John Muir NHS	California
Weir Farm NHS	Connecticut
De Soto N MEM	Florida
Frederick Law Olmsted NHS	Massachusetts
Longfellow House—Washington's Headquarters NHS	Massachusetts
Father Marquette N MEM	Michigan
Saint-Gaudens NHS	New Hamp.
Thomas Edison NHP	New Jersey
General Grant N MEM	New York
Kate Mullany NHS	New York
Thomas Cole NHS	New York
Vanderbilt Mansion NHS	New York
Women's Rights NHP	New York
Carl Sandburg Home NHS	North Carolina
Wright Brothers N MEM	North Carolina
Edgar Allan Poe NHS	Pennsylvania
Friendship Hill NHS	Pennsylvania
Roger Williams N MEM	Rhode Island
Sewall-Belmont House NHS	Wash., D.C.

Stories in the Rocks

Under your feet, under the grass, is the earth and stone. People study the earth — the geology — of the national parks to learn about how the earth was formed and what changes might come in the future. Will volcanoes erupt? Will earthquakes strike? How long can the tallest mountains stand up to wind and water?

PARKS VISITED

	PARK NAME	STATE
☐	Aniakchak NM & PRES	Alaska
☐	Bering Land Bridge N PRES	Alaska
☐	Katmai NP & PRES	Alaska
☐	Chiricahua NM	Arizona
☐	Grand Canyon NP	Arizona
☐	Sunset Crater Volcano NM	Arizona
☐	Devils Postpile NM	California
☐	Lassen Volcanic NP	California

	PARK NAME	STATE
☐	Lava Beds NM	California
☐	Pinnacles NP	California
☐	Black Canyon of the Gunnison NP	Colorado
☐	Great Sand Dunes NP & PRES	Colorado
☐	Hawaii Volcanoes NP	Hawaii
☐	Craters of the Moon NM	Idaho
☐	Mammoth Cave NP	Kentucky
☐	Glacier NP	Montana
☐	Capulin Volcano NM	New Mexico
☐	Carlsbad Caverns NP	New Mexico
☐	El Malpais NM	New Mexico
☐	White Sands NM	New Mexico
☐	Crater Lake NP	Oregon
☐	Oregon Caves NM	Oregon
☐	Badlands NP	South Dakota
☐	Jewel Cave NM	South Dakota
☐	Wind Cave NP	South Dakota
☐	Arches NP	Utah
☐	Bryce Canyon NP	Utah
☐	Canyonlands NP	Utah
☐	Cedar Breaks NM	Utah
☐	Natural Bridges NM	Utah
☐	Rainbow Bridge NM	Utah
☐	Timpanogos Cave NM	Utah
☐	Zion NP	Utah
☐	Ice Age Nat'l Scientific Reserve	Wisconsin
☐	Devils Tower NM	Wyoming
☐	Yellowstone NP	Wyoming

Stories of Industry

National parks conserve the stories of the industries that built America — from the great railroad industry that connected the east and west, to the automobile industry that gave us each our own wheels. Come learn about whaling, mining, and ranching. Hear the stories of some of America's great inventors. It's all here for you.

PARKS VISITED

	PARK NAME	STATE
☐	San Francisco Maritime NHP	California
☐	Lowell NHP	Massachusetts
☐	New Bedford Whaling NHP	Massachusetts
☐	Salem Maritime NHS	Massachusetts
☐	Saugus Iron Works NHS	Massachusetts
☐	Automobile Nat'l Heritage Area	Michigan
☐	Keweenaw NHP	Michigan
☐	Grant-Kohrs Ranch NHS	Montana
☐	Thomas Edison NHP	New Jersey
☐	Dayton Aviation Heritage NHP	Ohio
☐	Allegheny Portage Railroad NHS	Pennsylvania
☐	Hopewell Furnace NHS	Pennsylvania
☐	Steamtown NHS	Pennsylvania

Vietnam Veterans Memorial

Memories

National memorials help us remember important stories from America's past. Not all of the stories are happy ones. Memorials remind us of those who gave their lives for the nation's freedom in war, and those who served the country in other ways. Monuments help us remember, think, and learn.

PARKS VISITED

PARK NAME	STATE
☐ Oklahoma City N MEM	Oklahoma
☐ Flight 93 N MEM	Pennsylvania
☐ Johnstown Flood N MEM	Pennsylvania
☐ Arlington National Cemetery	Virginia
☐ Korean War Veterans Memorial	Wash., D.C.
☐ National Mall & Memorial Parks	Wash., D.C.
☐ Vietnam Veterans Memorial	Wash., D.C.

Stories of the Ocean and Shore

Did you know there are national parks underwater? The ocean has a landscape just as colorful and full of life as the land. These parks help conserve that landscape — the Earth's last frontier. Visit these parks to learn stories of the sea and the land, and the creatures that live there.

Channel Islands NP

PARKS VISITED

	PARK NAME	STATE
☐	Glacier Bay NP	Alaska
☐	Kenai Fjords NP	Alaska
☐	Channel Islands NP	California
☐	Point Reyes NS	California
☐	Biscayne NP	Florida
☐	Canaveral NS	Florida
☐	Dry Tortugas NP	Florida
☐	Cumberland Island NS	Georgia
☐	Assateague Island NS	Maryland

PARK NAME	STATE
Cape Cod NS	Massachusetts
Gulf Islands NS	Mississippi
Fire Island NS	New York
Cape Hatteras NS	North Carolina
Cape Lookout NS	North Carolina
Padre Island NS	Texas
Buck Island Reef NM	Virgin Islands
Virgin Islands NP	Virgin Islands
Virgin Islands Coral Reef NM	Virgin Islands

Dry Tortugas NP

FUN FACT: *New ocean conservation areas at Dry Tortugas NP and Point Reyes NS will help us understand the fragile underwater environments.*

Stories of the Natural World

Nature is always around us, but it snuggles close to us in these parks. The parks on this list protect areas of amazing beauty, rare plants and animals, and breathtaking scenery. In these parks the "circle of life" is all around you. Here there are plants and animals yet to be discovered. Will you be the first to see them?

PARKS VISITED

	PARK NAME	STATE
☐	Russell Cave NM	Alabama
☐	Alagnak Wild River	Alaska
☐	Denali NP & PRES	Alaska
☐	Gates of the Arctic NP	Alaska
☐	Kobuk Valley NP	Alaska
☐	Lake Clark NP & PRES	Alaska
☐	Noatak N PRES	Alaska
☐	Wrangell-St. Elias NP & PRES	Alaska
☐	National Park of American Samoa	Amer. Samoa

	PARK NAME	STATE
☐	Organ Pipe Cactus NM	Arizona
☐	Saguaro NP	Arizona
☐	Death Valley NP	California
☐	Joshua Tree NP	California
☐	Kings Canyon NP	California
☐	Mojave N PRES	California
☐	Muir Woods NM	California
☐	Redwood NP	California
☐	Yosemite NP	California
☐	Colorado NM	Colorado
☐	Rocky Mountain NP	Colorado
☐	Everglades NP	Florida
☐	Chattahoochee River NRA	Georgia
☐	Indiana Dunes NL	Indiana
☐	Tallgrass Prairie N PRES	Kansas
☐	Acadia NP	Maine
☐	Catoctin Mountain Park	Maryland
☐	Chesapeake & Ohio Canal NHP	Maryland
☐	Isle Royale NP	Michigan
☐	Pictured Rocks NL	Michigan
☐	Sleeping Bear Dunes NL	Michigan
☐	Natchez Trace Parkway	Mississippi
☐	Great Basin NP	Nevada
☐	Pinelands N RES	New Jersey
☐	Blue Ridge Parkway	North Carolina
☐	Cuyahoga Valley NP	Ohio
☐	Delaware Water Gap NRA	Pennsylvania
☐	Upper Delaware SRR	Pennsylvania

PARKS VISITED	PARK NAME	STATE
☐	Congaree NP	South Carolina
☐	Obed WSR	Tennessee
☐	Big Thicket N PRES	Texas
☐	Marsh-Billings-Rockefeller NHP	Vermont
☐	George Washington Memorial Parkway	Virginia
☐	Prince William Forest Park	Virginia
☐	Shenandoah NP	Virginia
☐	Mount Rainier NP	Washington
☐	North Cascades NP	Washington
☐	Olympic NP	Washington
☐	Kenilworth Park and Aquatic Gardens	Wash., D.C.
☐	Rock Creek Park	Wash., D.C.
☐	Apostle Islands NL	Wisconsin
☑	Grand Teton NP	Wyoming
☐	John D. Rockefeller, Jr. Memorial Parkway	Wyoming

FUN FACT: *The largest national park is Wrangell-St. Elias National Park and Preserve (Alaska) at more than 13 million acres.*

Wrangell-St. Elias NP & PRES

Family Fun

These parks offer an opportunity to get outside and play. Many are near lakes or rivers for swimming and boating. Others have a variety of activities all in one place — history, nature, recreation, and learning! Come visit and write your own story of adventure.

PARKS VISITED

PARK NAME	STATE
Golden Gate NRA	California
Santa Monica Mountains NRA	California
Whiskeytown-Shasta-Trinity NRA	California
Curecanti NRA	Colorado
Greenbelt Park	Maryland
Piscataway Park	Maryland
Boston Harbor Islands NRA	Massachusetts
Lake Mead NRA	Nevada
Gateway NRA	New York
Chickasaw NRA	Oklahoma
Big South Fork NRRA	Tennessee
Amistad NRA	Texas
Lake Meredith NRA	Texas
Wolf Trap NP for the Performing Arts	Virginia
Lake Roosevelt NRA	Washington
Ross Lake NRA	Washington
Gauley River NRA	West Virginia

Golden Spike NHS

Stories of the West

These parks let you travel west to the days before planes or cars. Learn about the life of a fur trapper when the West was really wild. Retrace the steps of Lewis and Clark. Join a wagon train headed for Oregon. Stake your claim in a gold rush or ride the steam train west to find a family homestead.

PARKS VISITED

PARK NAME	STATE
☐ Coronado N MEM	Arizona
☐ Arkansas Post N MEM	Arkansas
☐ Fort Smith NHS	Arkansas
☐ Bent's Old Fort NHS	Colorado
☐ City of Rocks N RES	Idaho
☐ Fort Larned NHS	Kansas
☐ Fort Scott NHS	Kansas
☐ Cumberland Gap NHP	Kentucky
☐ Grand Portage NM	Minnesota
☐ Jefferson Nat'l Expansion MEM	Missouri

	PARK NAME	STATE
☐	Chimney Rock NHS	Nebraska
☐	Homestead NM of America	Nebraska
☐	Scotts Bluff NM	Nebraska
☐	El Morro NM	New Mexico
☐	Fort Union Trading Post NHS	North Dakota
☐	Lewis and Clark NHP	Oregon
☐	Golden Spike NHS	Utah
☐	Fort Vancouver NHS	Washington
☐	Whitman Mission NHS	Washington
☐	Fort Laramie NHS	Wyoming

Bent's Old Fort NHS

FUN FACT: *The completion of the first transcontinental railroad is celebrated at Golden Spike National Historic Site, Utah, where the Central Pacific and the Union Pacific Railroads met.*

Military Stories

America has not always been at peace. Parks with stories of war or defense remind us to cherish that peace. Come and hear about the way the nation was formed, and the real price of freedom.

PARKS VISITED

	PARK NAME	STATE
☐	Horseshoe Bend NMP	Alabama
☐	Fort Bowie NHS	Arizona
☐	Castillo de San Marcos NM	Florida
☐	Fort Caroline N MEM	Florida
☐	Fort Matanzas NM	Florida
☐	Fort Frederica NM	Georgia
☐	Springfield Armory NHS	Massachusetts
☐	Fort Union NM	New Mexico
☐	Castle Clinton NM	New York
☐	Governors Island NM	New York
☐	Fort Raleigh NHS	North Carolina
☐	Perry's Victory and International Peace Memorial	Ohio
☐	Fort Necessity NB	Pennsylvania
☐	San Juan NHS	Puerto Rico
☐	Minuteman Missile NHS	South Dakota
☐	Fort Davis NHS	Texas
☐	Palo Alto Battlefield NHP	Texas
☐	Christiansted NHS	Virgin Islands

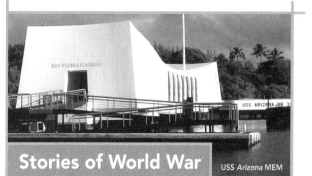

Stories of World War

USS *Arizona* MEM

These parks help tell the story of World War II. They include stories of the battles in the Pacific Islands and stories of hard work here at home. Do you know that thousands of Japanese Americans were held in camps in the United States during the war? That story is told here too. Come visit and learn more.

PARKS VISITED

PARK NAME	STATE
Manzanar NHS	California
Port Chicago Nav Mag N MEM	California
Rosie the Riveter/ World War II Homefront NHP	California
War in the Pacific NHP	Guam
World War II Valor in the Pacific NM	Hawaii
Minidoka NHS	Idaho
American Memorial Park	Saipan
World War II Memorial	Wash., D.C.

MY JUNIOR RANGER PROGRAMS

The **Junior Ranger Program** lets you explore your national parks at your own pace, with an activity book to guide you to the coolest stories in the park. Complete the book to earn a badge or patch and certificate. Each park program is different. When you visit a park, look for the Ranger Hat logo or ask a park ranger how to get started.

Arches NP

JUNIOR RANGER
EXPLORE · LEARN · PROTECT

Junior Ranger Programs I have completed:

Park Name	Date·
Mesa V...	
Yellowstone	
Yo...	

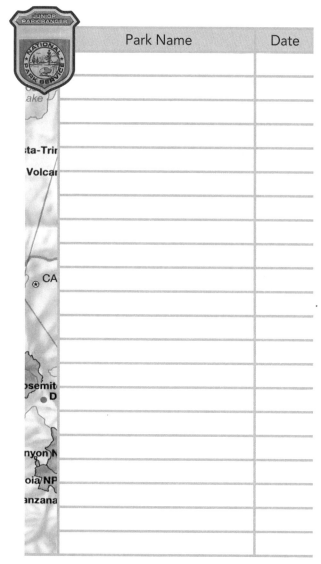

Park Name	Date

Park Name	Date

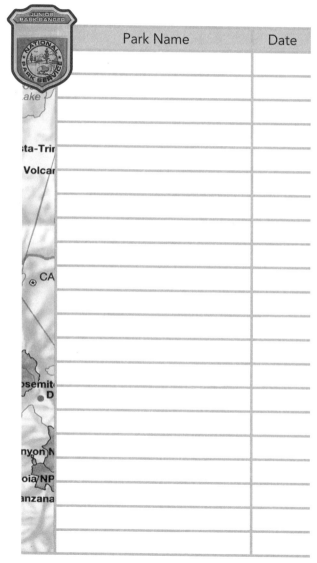

Park Name	Date

Park Name	Date

NATIONAL PARK SERVICE

ake

ta-Trir

Volcar

⊛ CA

semit
D

nyon N

oia NP

anzana

Park Name	Date

Park Name	Date

Park Name	Date

Rangers and park scientists keep field journals to help them remember their days in the out-of-doors. Some use journals to describe things they have seen — a beautiful sunrise or a special visitor. Others use journals to record measurements and other information about plants, animals, or rocks they are studying in the park.

Sometimes, when they get older, people even publish their journals as books, so everyone can share what they have learned.

Just like a real park ranger, you can use your journal to help remember your days in the park. You can record anything you think is special about your visit.

FUN FACT: *Eight national park areas preserve the works of great American artists and writers.*

57

FIELD JOURNAL

For each entry, begin by writing the date and where you are. Then record what is important to you.

Here are **Five Quick Questions** to help you with your journal. When you don't know what to write, find a spot, sit down, and ask yourself:

- What can I **see?**
- What can I **hear?**
- What can I **smell?**
- If I were here 100 or even 1,000 years ago, what would I see, hear, and smell?
- What does this place **mean** to me?

Vol

⊛

osen

anyo

uoia

1anza

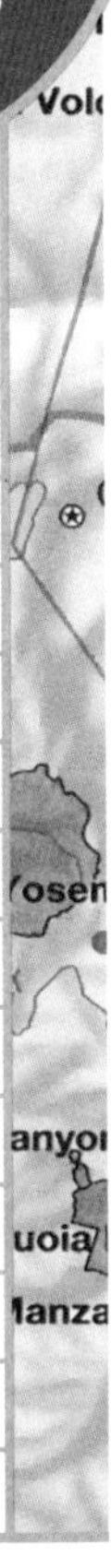

FUN FACT: *40 million years of the history of mammals is preserved in fossils at John Day Fossil Beds National Monument in Oregon.*

FUN FACT: The statue of Abraham Lincoln in the Lincoln Memorial in Washington, D.C., is 19 feet tall.

MY LISTS

Do you like to keep lists? Many park rangers and park visitors keep lists to remind them of the different kinds of birds, plants, and animals they see in the parks. Some keep these lists for years and years. They record every kind of bird or animal they see, and their list becomes a *"Life List"* — a list of all the types of birds or other creatures they have seen in their lives.

You can keep a list of anything. What are you interested in? Bears? Mountains? Rocks? Buildings? Keep a list of other important things you have seen!

On the following pages there are spaces for you to keep a bird list, a plant list, and a mammal list to get you started. There are also spaces for you to create your own lists.

MY BIRD LIST

List the bird's name (ask a
ranger if you do not know), the
date, and where you saw the bird.

Bird Name	Date	Where?

Bird Name	Date	Where?

MY MAMMAL LIST

List the animal's name (ask a ranger if you do not know), the date, and where you saw the mammal.

Mammal Name	Date	Where?

Mammal Name	Date	Where?

What is a Mammal?

Mammals are warm-blooded animals with furry coats. Mammals do not lay eggs. People are mammals, and so are bears, deer, rabbits, and bats (to name a few). How many kinds of mammals will you see?

MY PLANT & TREE LIST

List the plant's name (ask a ranger if you do not know), the date, and where you saw the plant or tree.

Plant/Tree Name	Date	Where?

Plant/Tree Name	Date	Where?

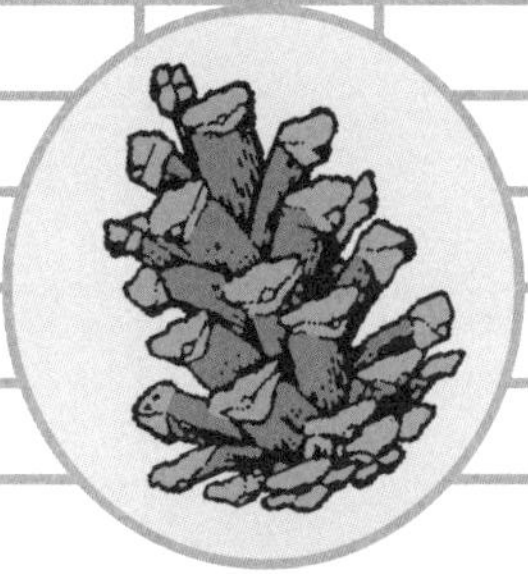

MY OWN LIST OF:

_____

Ask a ranger if you do not know what something is called. Be sure to record what it is, the date, and where you saw it.

Name	Date	Where?

Name	Date	Where?

MY OWN LIST OF:

Ask a ranger if you do not know what something is called. Be sure to record what it is, the date, and where you saw it.

Name	Date	Where?

Name	Date	Where?

I told my mom not to pick the flowers!

I planted flowers in the same garden people used 100 years ago!

HOW DID I HELP?

What did you do to help accomplish the mission of the National Park Service?

Write what you did, the date, and where you were.

I picked up trash around the campground.

What I Did to Help	Date	Where?

HOW DID I HELP?

What I Did to Help	Date	Where?

Be sure to ask a ranger what you can do to help the parks even when you are at home!

MY RANGER AUTOGRAPHS

MY RANGER AUTOGRAPHS

MY RANGER AUTOGRAPHS

MY RANGER AUTOGRAPHS

FUN FACT: *The first national park, Yellowstone, was created in 1872. The United States Cavalry (soldiers on horseback) were the first caretakers.*

USNPS

PEOPLE I MET

Here is a place for the autographs of other people you meet on your park visits. These could be new friends, other Junior Rangers, or other visitors.

se
ke

-Trin
olcan

CAF

emite
De

FUN FACT: *The highest point in North America, Mt. McKinley at 20,320 feet, is in Denali National Park and Preserve, Alaska.*

WHAT'S A WEBRANGER?

Now you can be a Junior Ranger even if you are not able to visit a national park. You will become a member of a growing group of young people who are interested in the world around them and who are involved with their nation's heritage...the **WebRangers**!

Over 50,000 people in 185 countries have become WebRangers!

How Can I Become a WebRanger?

Visit the website to start your journey. Set up your ranger station and you're ready to explore your national parks! Help a baby sea turtle reach the sea... Be a spy...Find out what a powder monkey is...Drive a dogsled...Experience the life and death struggle of a puma. There are over 50 activities created just for you! By completing activities, you can earn a WebRangers patch, FREE!

Your parents can learn along with you as you explore the parks in this web-safe environment. No personal information is collected, and none is required to participate.

The activities illustrate principles of natural science and American history in new ways. Some teachers even count the activities for extra credit.

Check it out for yourself at:
www.nps.gov/webrangers/

Important Web Addresses:

http://www.nps.gov
This is the main website for the
National Park Service. Visit the site to
plan your visit or to find out more
about your amazing national parks.

http://www.nps.gov/webrangers
Come on over and join the
thousands of people around the
world who are becoming
WebRangers.

http://www.nps.gov/kidszone
Park fun activities and print and play
materials are all right here in the
Kidszone.

http://www.nps.gov/learn
The place to learn about your
national parks.

http://www.nps.gov/volunteer
Search for opportunities to help take
care of your national parks.